Look at the letters and say the sounds. See how quickly you can say all of them.

Say the word *pen* and listen out for the sounds: *pen* – /p-e-n/. (There is one sound dot underneath the pen for each sound in the word.)

## Tips for teachers and parents

- **Sound dots**

  Some of the pages in this book have sound dots. Each of the dots represents a sound in the word illustrated above the dots. Say the word very slowly and clearly for the child, and then model sounding it out, pointing to each dot as you say the sound: for example, *cake* – /c-ai-k/. It is important to focus on the sounds in the word and not the letters used to spell it, so the sounds in *cake* are /c-ai-k/ and not /c-a-k-e/. The individual sounds in each sounding-out word are given in the instructions at the top of the page. After you have modelled sounding out a few times, the child will begin to hear the individual sounds without help.

- **Silent letters**

  Some English words have silent letters, such as the ‹e› in *gone*, which are not pronounced when the word is read. In these books, any silent letters are shown in faint type. Remind the child not to say the faint letters when blending the word.

- **‹s› saying /z/**

  The letter ‹s› is sometimes pronounced /z/: for example, at the ends of *is* and *his*. Children do not usually have trouble reading these words, but they might need some help and guidance at the beginning.

- **Vocabulary**

  If any vocabulary might be new to the child, ask what (s)he thinks it means. If (s)he does not know, point out the item in the picture, or explain the word and relate it to what is happening in the book.

# Little Word Books

**Little Word Books are fully decodable books for new readers.**

These Little Word Books have a very **carefully controlled vocabulary** and are specifically designed for children who are learning to read and write with *Jolly Phonics*. The text in the first two books uses only **decodable regular words** made up from the first group of letter sounds; the text in the next two books uses only the first and second groups of letter sounds and so on, so that the number of sounds used in the **text builds up cumulatively**.

**Faint type** is used for any silent letters, such as the ‹e› in *gone*.

**This book contains the following letter sounds:**

| Group 1: | s | a | t | i | p | n |
|---|---|---|---|---|---|---|
| Group 2: | c | k | e | h | r | m | d |
| Group 3: | g | o | u | l | f | b |
| Group 4: | ai | j | oa | ie | ee | or |
| Group 5: | z | w | ng | v | oo | oo |
| Group 6: | y | x | ch | sh | th | th |
| Group 7: | qu | ou | oi | ue | er | ar |

All of the letter sounds used in this book are also shown on the front inside cover; these can be used as a quick practice activity before starting the book.

The other Little Word Book at this level is: **Ten Tents**.

## Jolly Learning Ltd

© Sara Wernham 2020 (text)  © Stu McLellan (Beehive Illustration) 2020 (illustrations)
Edited by Theresa Reynolds and Louise Van-Pottelsberghe

www.jollylearning.co.uk   info@jollylearning.co.uk

Tailours House, High Road, Chigwell, Essex, IG7 6DL, UK.  Tel: +44 20 8501 0405
82 Winter Sport Lane, Williston, VT 05495, USA.  Tel: +1-800-488-2665
Printed in China. All rights reserved.

ISBN 978-1-84414-617-8

Reference: JL6178

## Teachers and parents

Before tackling this Little Word Book, a child will need to be able to do the following:

- Say the sounds made by the letters shown below;
- Read (blend) regular words containing these letter sounds.

## Letter sounds

| s | a | t | i | p | n | ck |
|---|---|---|---|---|---|---|
| e | h | r | m | d | g | o |
| u | l | f | b | ai | j | oa |
| ie | ee | or | z | w | ng | v |
| oo | **oo** | y | x | ch | sh | th |
| th | qu | ou | oi | ue | er | ar |